McBROOM's
ALMANAC

McBroom Books

McBroom and the Beanstalk
McBroom Tells a Lie
McBroom and the Great Race
McBroom's Ghost
McBroom Tells the Truth
McBroom's Zoo
McBroom's Ear
McBroom the Rainmaker
McBroom and the Big Wind
McBroom's Almanac

and Other Books by Sid Fleischman

Mr. Mysterious & Company
By the Great Horn Spoon!
The Ghost in the Noonday Sun
Chancy and the Grand Rascal
Longbeard the Wizard
Jingo Django
The Wooden Cat Man
The Ghost on Saturday Night
Mr. Mysterious's Secrets of Magic
Me and the Man on the Moon-Eyed Horse
Humbug Mountain
The Hey Hey Man

McBROOM's ALMANAC

Containing **TRUTHFUL** Accounts
of **AMAZING** Happenings
on **McBROOM's WONDERFUL ONE-ACRE FARM**,
to which are added
ASTOUNDING World Records,
INFALLIBLE Weather Signs & Predictions,
Useful Advice (**FULLY** Guaranteed),

MIRACULOUS Inventions
&
SUNDRY Jollifications

 SID FLEISCHMAN

Illustrated by Walter Lorraine

An Atlantic Monthly Press Book
Little, Brown and Company
BOSTON   TORONTO

TEXT COPYRIGHT © 1984 BY SID FLEISCHMAN

ILLUSTRATIONS COPYRIGHT © 1984 BY WALTER LORRAINE

Third Printing

Library of Congress Cataloging in Publication Data

Fleischman, Sid, 1920–
  McBroom's almanac.

  "An Atlantic Monthly Press book."
  Summary: Entries in McBroom's almanac include
farm tips, how-to's, McProverbs, nature lore, cartoons
and McBroom's Calendar of Important Dates.
  [1. Tall tales.   2. Almanacs — Wit and humor]
I. Lorraine, Walter H., ill.   II. Title.
PZ7.F5992Mae 1984   [Fic]   83-9043
ISBN 0-316-26009-6
ISBN 0-316-26011-8 (pbk.)

ATLANTIC—LITTLE, BROWN BOOKS
ARE PUBLISHED BY
LITTLE, BROWN AND COMPANY
IN ASSOCIATION WITH
THE ATLANTIC MONTHLY PRESS

BP

Published simultaneously in Canada
by Little, Brown & Company (Canada) Limited

PRINTED IN THE UNITED STATES OF AMERICA

For
Linalansteveandetta

McBROOM'S CALENDAR
OF IMPORTANT DATES

January 23 SNOWMAN DOWNHILL SKIING COMPETITION

February 7 SCHOOL SPELLING BEE. First student to teach a bee to spell, wins.

March 16 NELLY T. AMBLESIDE DAY. Commemorates the first woman to successfully grow mashed potatoes. She planted them with a sledgehammer.

April 5 WHITE ELEPHANT SALE. (Whitewashed elephants will be disqualified).

April 9 ANNUAL SNORING CONTEST has been canceled. The thundering ruckus last year busted all the courthouse windows and derailed a freight train.

May 31 PRAIRIE ROAD PULLING DAY. Muddy roads shrink when they dry out. Men, women, and children grab the ends of the roads and stretch them back to length.

June 5 FLEA GUESSING CONTEST. Person able to guess the number of fleas on Toby, the town dog, gets to keep them.

July 13 BIRTHDAY OF SOWBELLY SMITH, the first man on the prairie to take a bath. Band concert on courthouse steps.

August 24 STATE ROOSTER CROWING COMPETITION. Bring earplugs.

September 5 SCHOOL BLACKBOARD EVENT. Student who can stay in the classroom the longest, while chalk and fingernails are scratched across the blackboard, wins a day's homework. The teacher must do it.

October 11 ANNIVERSARY OF THE DAY THE MAYOR'S WIFE WENT MUSHROOM HUNTING. Flags flown at half-mast.

October 19 UGLIEST HOG CONTEST. The first snouty face to sour a pan of milk, wins. Spectators are advised to wear blindfolds.

November 27 NEEDLE THREADING COMPETITION. Held in the dark.

December 15 ANNUAL SCHOOL PLAY begins. No one goes to school and everyone plays.

JANUARY

A dust of snow, a dash of sleet —
Expect no more'n forty feet.

How to Keep Warm All Winter
with One Stick of Wood

Choose a stick of wood about one inch in diameter and eighteen inches long. Fold a newspaper and place it in a pocket.

At the start of cold weather, hurl the stick due south with all your might. Run after the stick at full speed, pick it up, and fling it again. You will begin to warm up.

Repeat flinging and fetching the stick, always in a southerly direction. When you reach a climate that calls for fanning yourself with the newspaper, throw away the stick.

JANUARY

Snowflakes? We get some mighty big ones out here on the prairie. Regular world-beaters.

January is the best month for outsized snowflakes. But how folks exaggerate!

The widow lady down the road claims she starches 'em and irons 'em and uses 'em for fancy tablecloths. The *big* ones she uses for bed sheets.

Well, that's a ring-tailed falsehood. The only time I heard her tell the truth, her mouth was shut.

We had a fall of snow yesterday, but the flakes were downright puny. The storm gave me a chance to catch up on my inside chores. And one of them was to make my New Year's resolution. I even wrote it out so I wouldn't forget:

"I, Josh McBroom, hereby resolve to stick to the untarnished, unvarnished truth for the next twelve months. If I stray from a single fact, I hope to sit on a flagpole."

I signed it with a flourish and put aside my pen. Now, I hadn't been able to find an unused sheet of writing paper in the house. The young'uns had used up every scrap doing homework.

The untarnished, unvarnished truth is that I wrote up my resolution on one of those puny, white prairie snowflakes. I ripped off the other half to use as blotting paper.

Mrs. McBroom's Energy-saving Recipe for Boiling Eggs

This method requires no fire.
Fill a pan with a quart of water.
Drop in sixteen hot chili peppers.
The peppers will bring the water
    to a simmer in nine minutes flat.
Drop in eggs. Boil until done.

Prairie Spider

Avoid the junk-eatin' spider,
With all the junk inside her.
She dines on nails and carpet tacks;
She's meaner than a choppin' ax.
Her silk'll rip your best attire —
She spins her webs of pure barbed wire.

— Will McBroom

January is a bad month to paint your barn.

6

FEBRUARY

Rowdy storms, cold and gruff;
A week of Feb. is quite enough.

How to Make Your Own Flashlight

1. Save an empty soup can.
2. Wait for spring weather — it changes quicker'n a chameleon on a checkerboard. Wait for a balmy night that draws out the insects.

3. A sudden icy blast is sure to come along. It'll catch those bugs by surprise.
4. Collect two- or three-dozen critters in your soup can. But not any critters.
5. Just the lightning bugs that froze with their lights on.

It's not generally known, but I invented air conditioning. I read in the paper the idea has already spread to the big cities.

But, shucks, everyone is welcome to it. Folks around here call it McBroom's Natural Winter Extract & Relief for the Summer Dismals. You can make your own, same as us.

February is about the last month you can lay in a supply of prime Winter Extract.

Wait for an infernal cold day. When the mercury in the thermometer drops to the bottom — you're getting close. But the weather's still a mite too warm.

9

When the mercury busts the glass bulb and rolls over to the fireplace to get warm — that's Extract weather.

"Will*jill*hester*chester*peter*polly*tim*tom*mary *larry*and-little*clarinda!*" I shouted to our young'uns. "Bulb's shattered. Fetch the ripsaws, the crosscut saws, and let's get to work!"

Cold? Mercy, it was so cold outside *the wind had frozen solid.*

Didn't we get busy! We began sawing up chunks of frozen wind.

Now, you got to do the thing right. Wind's got a grain, just like wood. So be positive to use the crosscut saw against the grain, and the ripsaw along with it.

It fell dark before we finished harvesting and hauling that Winter Extract to our icehouse. And there stood our neighbor Heck Jones. That skinflint is so mean and miserly he brands the horseflies over at his place for fear someone will rustle 'em.

"Are you hidin' my left sock, McBroom?" he asked.

"Of course not," I said.

"Someone stole it off the clothesline. My best black sock, too! It only had three holes in it. If I catch the thief, I'll have him in a court of law!"

He loped away, grumbling and snarling.

We finished packing sawdust around the chunks of wind to keep them frozen. "Good work, my lambs," I said. "We're all set for the Summer Dismals."

Well, Heck Jones walked around in one sock the rest of winter, and summer, too.

As soon as the days turned sizzle-hot, we'd set a chunk of Winter Extract in the parlor. In a second or three it

would begin to thaw — just a cool breeze at first. But when that February wind really got whistling, it would lift the curtains!

One hot night I fetched in a nice chunk of frozen wind without bothering to scrape off the sawdust. A few minutes later I saw a black thing shoot across the room. Something had got frozen in our Winter Extract.

"Heck Jones's sock!" I declared. "I can smell his feet!"

He was sure to think we'd stolen it. He'd have us in a court of law! I made a grab for it, but the February wind

McPROVERB

It's more blessed to give than to receive — unless you have chicken pox.

was kicking up such a blow it shot the sock past the curtains and far out the window.

I could see Heck Jones asleep in his hammock, one sock on, the other foot bare. The left sock hoisted its tail like a kite in the air and started down.

I declare, if I didn't see it with my own eyes, I'd think I was scrambly-witted. That holey black sock had the instinct of a homing pigeon. It returned right to Heck Jones's left foot and pulled itself on. I think it navigated by scent.

What Heck Jones thought when he awoke and looked at both feet — I can't reckon.

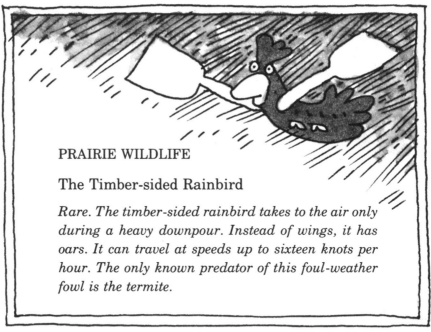

PRAIRIE WILDLIFE

The Timber-sided Rainbird

Rare. The timber-sided rainbird takes to the air only during a heavy downpour. Instead of wings, it has oars. It can travel at speeds up to sixteen knots per hour. The only known predator of this foul-weather fowl is the termite.

Don't paint your barn in February,  either.

M A R C H

Wind will be a wild travail;
Fly your kite with a chain-link tail.

McBroom's Painless Cold Remedy

To cure the common cold make a tonic of the following ingredients: six parsnips, eleven onions, a pint of molasses, three gallons of rainwater, a dill pickle, and the head of a mackerel. Simmer on top of the stove for seven days, then make a dozen brownies.

By this time your cold will be gone, and you won't have to take the tonic. But you will be hungry. Eat the brownies.

MARCH

This is the month to paint your barn!

Out here on our wonderful one-acre farm, we don't use paintbrushes and ladders and elbow lard. Gracious, no. The young'uns found an easier way.

That must have been three-four summers ago, when we lost our tin funnel.

Now, that topsoil of ours is so rich it'll grow *anything,* and faster'n double-quick. It didn't take long to find that funnel. It had got covered over during the plowing, and it came busting through our topsoil. By the time we could snatch it out of the ground, that funnel looked like a tin wigwam with a handle — it had grown that big.

15

We hung it in the barn and near forgot about it.

The following March the snow had melted, the sun had come out, and I reckoned the barn could use a coat of paint.

"Willjillhesterchesterpeterpollytimtommarylarryand- littleclarinda!" I called. "Start scraping off the old paint. I'll go to town for supplies."

I couldn't have been gone more'n an hour and six minutes. When I returned I could hardly believe my eyes. Glory be! — the young'uns had scraped and chipped off every speck of old paint. And they were passing the time with a stout rope, knotted at the ends, playing tug-o'- war.

"How'd you get the job done so uncommon fast?" I asked.

They only laughed and giggled among themselves, and went on with their game of tug-o'-war.

"We'll paint tomorrow," I said, unloading buckets of red barn paint. "It's turned a mite too windy."

I don't have to tell you that the wind does kick up a bit in the month of March. I've seen so many hats in the air they fly in formation like migrating birds. While I was in town, a gust came along so powerful strong —

If you don't like soup, the best way to eat it is with a fork.

— Larry McBroom

well, you know that bronze statue of Abraham Lincoln in front of the courthouse? The March wind blew his hat off.

You can't paint in weather like that, so I took myself a nap. When I got up the young'uns were still haulin' away at tug-o'-war. But the barn had a spanking new coat of red paint on it!

Those scamps. They'd figured out a way to get the March wind to do the work.

The secret is that giant funnel. First, they'd thrown

17

grit in the big end, caught the wind, and sandblasted the barn.

Next came the paint. With window screen fixed over the spout, they'd lifted the funnel until the flared end caught a blast of wind. Whoooosh! Out came the red stuff. The rascals had *spray painted* the barn!

My, doesn't the March wind come in useful! I forgot to tell you the young'uns were all at one end of their tug-o'-war rope. The *wind* was tuggin' on the knot at the other end.

FARM *TIP*

It's poor advice to plant potatoes in the dark of the moon. Better to plant them in the garden.

To stop the hiccups, wrap your neck with an old stocking soaked in skunk oil.
— Tim McBroom

I'd rather have hiccups.
— Mary McBroom

APRIL

Mud (a dipstick will reveal)
hub deep to a Ferris wheel.

APRIL

It's planting time, and I see that Heck Jones is putting in another crop of carrots. That hardscrabble farm of his is so worn out it takes a full acre to raise one skinny, scrawny carrot. And his carrots grow so crooked, come harvest time, he has to twist 'em out of the ground. He sells them as corkscrews.

But he's up to some new mischief. Why else is that infernal neighbor of ours offering a nickel apiece for woodpeckers?

Well! Every boy and girl in the county is out with bird nets catching those noisemakers. Even our own young'uns.

"He's got woodpeckers thicker'n flies in his barn," said

our oldest boy, Will. "I think he's trying to learn their language."

"Pa, why do you reckon he needs so *many* birds?" asked Jill.

I scratched my head. "You know how rock-hard his ground is. He has to pry it open with a crowbar to get a seed in. Maybe he figures he can talk those woodpeckers into drilling planting holes for him."

But I was way off the mark. Toward the end of April, Heck Jones came out of his barn. He had a sly smile on his face, and a flock of woodpeckers on his hat and shoulders. Tame as you please!

"Howdy, McBroom," he said. "Reckon I'll buy your farm. Not that it's worth a chaw of tobacco. A little ol' patch of ground — I've seen flea bites larger'n that."

"It's not for sale," I answered stiffly. He'd been trying to pry us off our wonderful one-acre farm for years.

"I'm feeling uncommon generous, McBroom. I'll give you a full twenty dollars and throw in a corkscrew."

I didn't like the hungry way those woodpeckers were eyeing our farm. "Heck Jones," I said. "Save your breath."

"You'll change your mind," he said, and laughed. "Hee-haw, McBroom. Sleep well."

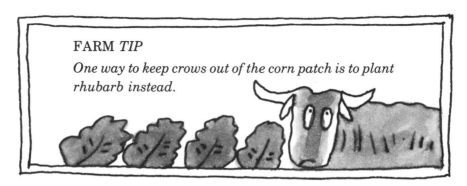

FARM *TIP*

One way to keep crows out of the corn patch is to plant rhubarb instead.

Sleep? We had hardly shut our eyes when there came a clatterwacking on the roof. It was those confounded woodpeckers! And when I jumped to the window, I could see more coming.

Heck Jones was turning his whole flock loose. I could see him in the moonlight, shutting the barn door and then pointing his long arm and finger our way.

I don't know how he did it, but he'd trained those noisy birds to attack.

Mercy, what a rip-roaring hammering and a ker-rap-tap-tap! It was loud enough to wake snakes. The very

Mc P R O V E R B

He who leaves no stone
unturned will have a sore
back.

Ode to a Frog

I never saw a frog as wise
as one we named Adella.
'Cause when the clouds would liquidize,
she'd carry an umbrella.

— Jill McBroom

To grow square turnips, study mathematics.
It tells all about square roots.

— Hester McBroom

26

MAY

Scented breezes, skunks outdoors;
They're not extinct, that's dinosaurs.

How to Plow a Garden
in Two Minutes Flat

Scatter and bury a sack of fresh bones. Then call the dogs.

M A Y

This is a mighty pleasant month to go canoeing.

Of course, you must get the craft balanced just right. I hope you won't make the mistake our boys did — unless you can swim.

We were fixin' to have a picnic down at the lake, and the boys hauled our canoe out of the barn. When they brushed off the cobwebs — mercy! How the mice had been gnawing away! That canoe had more holes in it than a wool shirt at a moth social.

"Young'uns," I said. "It'll take a week to mend. No canoe riding today."

"Aw-w-w, Pa," they groaned.

"Maybe we can grow us one," Chester said.

I scratched my head. We'd grown all nature of things in that amazing topsoil of ours, but I had my doubts. "Canoes don't naturally grow from seed, my lambs."

"Can we try, Pa?" asked Mary.

"If you hurry." I was already packing up the car with picnic baskets.

Didn't those scamps get busy! They reckoned a string bean was the right shape, and planted a seed.

The vine sprouted right up. The young'uns picked the little beans soon as they appeared — except one. All the git-up-and-go in the soil rushed into that lone bean.

I declare, if the thing didn't grow to canoe size in no

time. It would hold all the young'uns at one sitting, with room to spare!

But you know how string beans are. They grow tarnaciously crooked.

"My lambs," I said. "You got the right idea, but the wrong seed. You won't be able to paddle in anything but circles."

"We'll try a green pea," said Polly.

Well! In a minute or less they had themselves a fat pod straight as an arrow. They split it in two, prying out the boulder-size peas.

I gazed at the pods and smiled. "Looks like you grew yourselves a fine pair of canoes. Evenly matched!"

They'd got themselves a mite dusty, the young'uns,

and my dear wife Melissa said, "Now you wash up before we leave. And boys, don't forget to comb your hair."

We packed the pea-pod canoes on the roof of the car, and off we went.

The boys wanted one of the boats to themselves, so the girls took the other.

I made sure the young'uns were seated *exactly* along the center to keep an even balance, and shoved them off into the lake.

The girls sailed along as pretty as you please. But the boys were standing kneedeep in water. Their canoe had capsized.

"You've got to balance yourselves off as fine as a gold scale," I said.

"We did, Pa!" called Will. "Something must be wrong with our boat."

"Let me try," I said, and got in.

I wasn't a yard from shore when the canoe tipped over.

I knew what was wrong. I stood with my legs in the water and went through my pockets. Sure enough, I found two silver dollars in my right trouser pocket. They were throwing the canoe off balance.

As soon as I put one in the left pocket, and one in the right, I was able to skim right along.

I returned to shore. "Empty your pockets," I told the boys. "You must be out of balance with tops and marbles and stuff."

But there wasn't a top or a marble between them. Their pockets were empty.

And then I saw the trouble.

"Who's got a comb?" I said.

Mama had one, and I set to work. There was no way those boys could balance off the canoe the way they'd furrowed their hair — all on the left side.

It wasn't a moment before they were paddling all over the lake.

I'd parted their hair right down the middle.

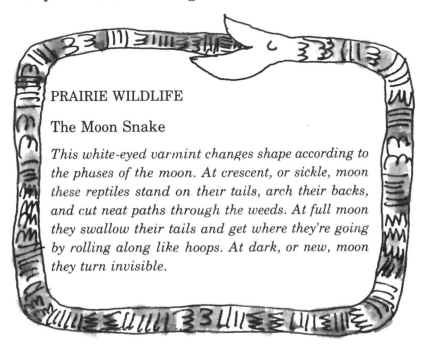

PRAIRIE WILDLIFE

The Moon Snake

This white-eyed varmint changes shape according to the phases of the moon. At crescent, or sickle, moon these reptiles stand on their tails, arch their backs, and cut neat paths through the weeds. At full moon they swallow their tails and get where they're going by rolling along like hoops. At dark, or new, moon they turn invisible.

Mc P R O V E R B

Don't follow the crowd. Everyone may be going to the dentist.

GROW ONE-TON WATERMELONS!

Visit McBroom's World Famous Wonderful One-Acre Farm. Try out our terrific topsoil for yourself. Plant a watermelon seed and stand back and watch! In one minute and fourteen seconds flat you'll grow a 2000 pounder. Guaranteed. Smaller ones we throw to the hogs.

Bring truck to cart it home. Eat your fill, and use the rest for a swimming pool.

JUNE

Mackerel skies — no use wishing;
There's a spot you can't go fishing.

Amazing Event!

Late this month, a heavy dust storm came along while Peter and Polly McBroom were outside playing catch with a potato. The spud got caught in the dust and sprouted lickety-zip. We got stepladders, reached up into the murky air, and harvested seven bushels of new potatoes.

Fireflies — A World Record

By actual count, 4,678,092,546,190,359,121 fireflies appeared on the seventeenth day of this month. Folks needed sunglasses to step outside at night.

J U N E

Heck Jones has let one of his corkscrew carrots go to seed for next year's crop. He'd been growing them so long he had himself a new strain — even the seeds were twistical.

We had begun to dig a new water well, me and the young'uns. Mighty hard work! The May flies were a month late and giving us a pesky time of it.

I disliked to do it, but I called on that rascally neighbor of ours. "Heck Jones," I said. "I want to buy a carrot seed."

"Can't hear you," he answered. He was wearing his

purple earmuffs, the woodpeckers were still hammering away in the attic — and he had a long piece of string hanging out of his mouth.

I lifted my voice to a shout. "What'll you take for a carrot seed?"

Heck didn't answer. He tied the loose end of the string to a doorknob. It was clear he had a powerful toothache.

"Slam the door and yank this infernal tooth, Mc-Broom."

It was the neighborly thing to do. But when I slammed the door, the string yanked Heck Jones off his feet. That tooth must have had a root that grew all the way down to China.

"Let me have a carrot seed and I'll pull out that tooth," I offered.

"You drive a hard bargain," he said with a yowl. "Agreed!"

My dear wife Melissa and the young'uns were mighty surprised to see me leading Heck Jones by that tooth string back to our farm.

"My lambs," I said. "Plant this seed where we started the well."

Once the carrot seed got a taste of our riproarious soil,

FARM *TIP*

When mosquitoes get big and pesky, catch 'em with rattraps.

the greens shot up like a spray of fireworks! And glory be! — the twistical carrot began drilling us a well!

"Ow-w-w-w!" Heck Jones groaned. "My tooth, Mc-Broom!"

I tied the loose end of the string around a kernel of corn and stamped it into our topsoil. "Hang on, Heck Jones," I said. "That fang is about to come flying out."

The corn stalk shot out of the ground with a jolt. The string tightened. The next thing I saw, Heck Jones was jerked out of his shoes and was hanging by a tooth three feet in the air.

"Catch his legs!" I called to the young'uns.

I'd never seen a hunk of jaw crockery so stubborn! We hung on to his legs and pulled. The corn stalk kept growing. The tooth didn't budge. And I forgot all about the corkscrew carrot drilling away.

How the battle raged! With all our weight at one end, the corn stalk was bent as taut as a bow. It must have been two hours before the fang came flying loose. We fell in a pile on the ground, Heck Jones on top of us.

Then he took off at a gallop without so much as a thank you.

We dusted ourselves off — but mercy! That carrot had grown six feet across at the shoulders. And it was still drilling away!

"Quick!" I said. "We've got to unscrew that monstropolous thing out of the ground."

But we were too late. It had grown too enormous big. Even with all of us twisting, that carrot wouldn't budge. No telling how far down it had drilled.

It was hardly a moment later that Jill gave a yell —

and I understood why Heck Jones had torn off in such a burnt hurry.

"Pa! Look! A tornado!"

"And heading straight this way!" said Polly.

We dove for the storm cellar. No doubt Heck Jones had spotted the twister from higher up on the corn stalk. That infernal neighbor hadn't bothered to warn us!

We had hardly got the cellar doors shut when the tornado came roaring in. I expected to have the house snatched off over our heads.

But my, weren't we lucky! That tornado didn't touch a thing, hardly.

When we climbed out of the storm cellar — well, my eyes about jumped out of my head. That fearsome twister had unscrewed the gigantical carrot clear out of the ground!

And carried it off. I found out later the tornado had run the thing through so many barbed-wire fences, it left a trail of sliced carrots across three states.

"I wonder how deep that hole in the ground is?" said Larry. He'd pitched in a stone, but we never did hear it touch bottom.

We kept that hole for months, laid over with chicken wire so nobody would fall in. Visitors came from all over to see the thing. And to listen to the mysterious voices rise up.

Finally, one feller came along who recognized the lingo. He said it was Chinese.

McP R O V E R B

When success goes to someone's head, it generally finds nothing there.

McBroom's Best Advice on How to Pet a Skunk

Don't.

PRAIRIE WILDLIFE

The Checkerback Flatfish

A useless, black and white fish — all skin and not even any bones. Heck Jones dries them and sells them as checkerboards.

WEATHER SIGN

It'll be a bad year for fleas if you catch a catfish wearing a flea collar.

J U L Y

———

Rain and shine, the sundial stands
Proclaiming smugly: "Look, no hands."

How to Keep a Gate from Squeaking

Jump over the fence.

Mrs. McBroom's Household Hints

Don't feed your chickens day-old bread.
They'll lay day-old eggs.

44

Lots of lightning bugs and mosquitoes out this time of year. The lightning bugs can be downright dangerous.

Take the Fourth of July. We'd gone to town for the fun and frolic when along came Bear-Eating John. He walks on a peg leg, and has a large spider tattooed on the end of his nose.

We don't see much of Bear-Eating John. He eats so much bear meat that he hibernates all winter.

He'd come out of the woods for the fireworks, and I could see he had brought some noisemakers of his own — a couple of sticks of dynamite in his hip pocket.

45

While the young'uns had gone over to the candy-eating contest Bear-Eating John and I sat on a bench with the judge and the mayor. Some folks call it the Liars' Bench — but there's no truth to that.

We slapped mosquitoes and swapped stories, waiting for night to fall and the fireworks to start.

"Bear-Eating John," said the mayor. "I can't help noticing that spider on the end of your nose. Never could. Not that it's any of my business —"

"I couldn't get a wink of sleep without it," replied the mountain man.

"I don't follow you," said the judge, whacking a mosquito on his neck.

"Well, sir, I snooze with my nose out of the blanket," Bear-Eating John explained. "That spider scares off the flies. And the lisquitoes, too."

"What in tarnation are lisquitoes?" I asked.

"Up in the woods, lightning bugs and mosquitoes have crossed. Those lisquitoes have mighty mean stingers — and their own headlights to find you at night."

We mulled that over for a bit, for natural history was entitled to serious thought and discussion. Then I said, "Bear-Eating John, have you ever tasted a mosquito?"

NATURE LORE

Out here on the prairie our state bird is the mosquito.

"Can't say I have, McBroom."

"Better'n frogs' legs and a lot more meat to the bone. Last year we had skeeters so big you needed a barn door to swat 'em. Folks used 'em for stew meat."

"I'll attest to that," remarked the judge.

"Yes, sir," I added. "Fried mosquito legs are considered a delicacy, and only served on Sundays."

"I'll attest to that," muttered the judge, nodding his head.

"I declare," said Bear-Eating John. "I didn't know your city mosquitoes grew so small. I used to log mosquitoes in the old days."

"Log 'em?" asked the mayor.

"For the timber. I found a place where mountain mosquitoes used to go to die. I got together a logging crew and we hauled out the stingers. Sold 'em for telephone poles."

Well, I couldn't let that pass, even though dark was falling, swarms of lightning bugs were out, and the fireworks show was about to start.

"Bear-Eating John," I said. "It's clear you've never laid eyes on a prime long-nosed prairie mosquito. Like the one that stung me two years ago over in Nebraska."

"What's so unusual about that, McBroom?"

"I was asleep in Iowa at the time."

Bear-Eating John jumped to his peg leg with a jolt of surprise. That's when I noticed the sticks of dynamite in his hip pocket were smoking and sputtering away. *Fireflies had lit the fuses!*

I grabbed the sticks and heaved them clear. "Run for your lives!"

Didn't we scramble off that bench in a hurry! The dynamite exploded right in the middle of the waiting stock of fireworks. My, what a show!

Not a soul got hurt, except that Bear-Eating John skinned the spider off his nose.

"McBroom," he said, after the excitement died down. "McBroom, it near took my breath away to hear you tell about that long-nosed prairie mosquito. I imagine there are some folks who might doubt your word. Well, I'll vouch for your truthfulness — I can produce the evidence."

"Evidence?" I asked.

"I shot down that same skeeter, McBroom." He tapped that polished peg leg of his. "I sawed off the merest tip of its stinger — and this is it."

I'm sorry to say it, but Bear-Eating John was given to stretching the truth. That peg leg of his had a knothole in it.

When I rounded up the young'uns for home, they were covered over with mosquito bites. But all the rest of summer we were not much bothered by the pesky varmints. The young'uns had eaten so much at the candy-eating contest that the skeeters developed cavities in their stingers.

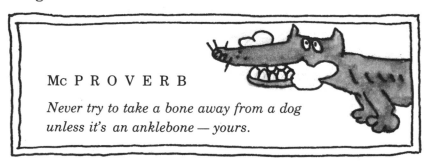

Mc P R O V E R B

Never try to take a bone away from a dog
unless it's an anklebone — yours.

WEATHER SIGN

If you discover moss growing on the south side of your trees, it's a sign that your compass is on the blink.

Don't pass a freshly painted fence with the sun behind you. Your shadow will stick tight.
— Clarinda McBroom

NATURE LORE

Cross a morning glory with an evening primrose, and you will get a lunch flower.

Mrs. McBroom's Household Hints

To scour a food-stuck frying pan, hold it out the window and wait for a sandstorm.

Good Deed

We grew a little cactus patch
for porcupines to come and scratch.
— Polly McBroom

AUGUST

Quick-dry heat a big complaint —
Will even shrink a coat of paint.

Extraordinary Happening!

August is a bad month for grasshoppers. But what happened this year beats all! At dawn one day, a horde of the hoplegs started across the sky and just about blocked out the sun. On they came, day after day, mile after mile of the varmints in a broad column.

It was a full week before we saw the last of them. And that's when we discovered what a good turn they'd done us. The winged critters had passed overhead in such huge numbers that their *shadows* had worn a path across the earth.

We're using it as a new county road.

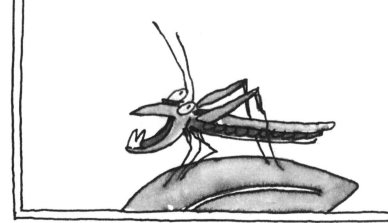

A U G U S T

This is an all-fired hot month. You don't need a calendar to tell you it's August. If you're hanging up the wash and the sun scorches the sheets before you can snap on clothespins — it's August.

The fifth day of the month is my birthday.

"Pa, why can't we bake you a cake?" asked Mary.

"You know how partial I am to Mama's four o'clock raisin bread," I answered. "That's birthday cake to me."

My dear wife Melissa had already started mixing the yeast and flour. That bread is something you can count on to the second — no matter what time you start, it's always done at four o'clock.

"I forgot the raisins," said Melissa. "Jill, take over the recipe. And Pa, stay out of the kitchen."

"I want to help," I heard Will say.

"Me, too," added the other young'uns, one after the other.

I went out back to check on my new irrigation system. I saw Melissa with clothespins to hang bunches of grapes on the wash line. But the day was so hot the grapes were puckering into raisins too perishing fast — they were drying up hard as gravel.

"Jill!" Melissa called.

Jill must have turned the recipe over to another young'un. In a moment she was following her mother, unsnapping raisins seconds after Melissa hung up grapes.

I was overjoyed to see my irrigation system dripping away, steady as a clock. We hadn't had a speck of rain in a month, but I'd found a way to beat the drought. I'd planted weeping willow trees, with a rain barrel under each one. And didn't those willows weep! The rain barrels were overflowing.

"Will! Chester! I called.

They came out of the kitchen, both licking dough off

NATURE LORE

If bees follow you into the house, it's a sign that you're about to break out with hives.

their fingers, and helped me empty the rain barrels into the irrigation ditches.

With lemonade to make and ice cream to crank, the young'uns were in and out of the kitchen. And they'd all taken turns mixing up the big batch of raisin bread.

The sun was well past overhead when Melissa came flying out the back door. She'd snatched up Little Clarinda in her arms. Some of the young'uns were at her heels. Others tumbled out of the windows as if something were chasing them.

And something was!

"Pa!" Melissa cried out. "I set the dough to rise, but something's gone wrong. Look!"

Merciful powers! The dough was swelling up like a cow with stomach colic — and still rising. Dough filled the windows. Dough pressed against the doors. I do believe in another moment it would have started to lift off the roof.

But glory be for that August weather! The blast-furnace heat turned our house into a seven-room oven. The dough stopped rising and began to bake.

Our roof was saved. And my, what a delicious smell came out the chimney! Folks must have been able to sniff that four o'clock raisin bread for miles around.

But how sorrowful my dear wife Melissa looked. I smiled and said, "It must be that crock of triple-strong yeast I started up."

"But I only used a dab," said Melissa.

Jill's eyebrows gave a jump. "Mama, I didn't know you mixed in the yeast. I did, too!"

"Same here!" said Will. "Just following the recipe."

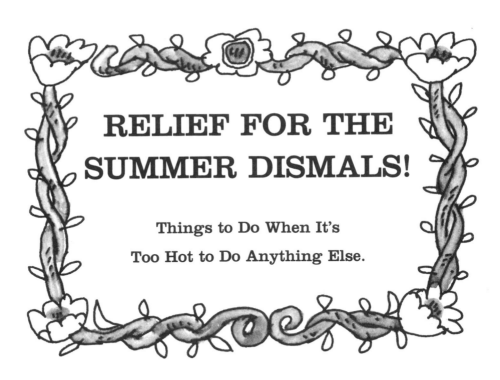

RELIEF FOR THE SUMMER DISMALS!

Things to Do When It's

Too Hot to Do Anything Else.

Make an automatic flyswatter.

Flies pestering you? Try this:

Step 1. Spear an ear of corn with a stick.

Step 2. Hold in sunlight. Corn will begin to pop.

Step 3. Bombardment of popcorn will swat flies at
up to thirty feet.

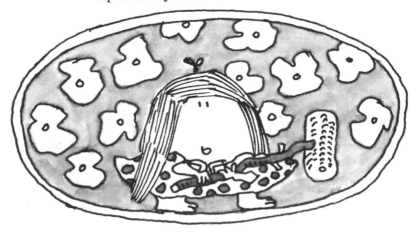

Hold a yelling contest.

How loud and fast can you yell "Willjillhesterchester-
peterpollytimtommarylarryandlittleclarinda!"

Teach a tadpole to swim.

It gets so dry out on the prairie some tadpoles have
never seen water. Find one in a dry creek bed and
dust it off. Take it in the bath with you. It may be
afraid of the water at first, so don't let go. Teach it
to float on its back, first. Then the dog paddle. By the
end of the summer dismals it will be doing high dives
off the soap dish.

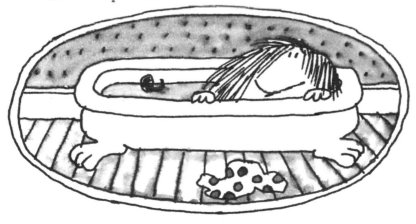

Artist

I drew a mousetrap with my paints,
And lost it near our house.
The picture looked so mighty real,
It snapped and caught a mouse.
                    — Chester McBroom

PRAIRIE WILDLIFE

Goggle Grouse

A variety of prairie chicken that appears during dry
weather. They hide from hunters by beating their wings
to raise great clouds of dust. They are born with gog-
gles that keep the dust out of their eyes.

SEPTEMBER

When back to school,
You just can't win.
Comes rain — you're out;
Comes sun — you're in.

Biggest Flea — A World Record

The bloodsucking varmint was discovered feeding on a stand of dogwood trees. It was first sighted on the night of August 2 by Chester McBroom, who mistook it for a rhinoceros. We never could catch the thing to weigh it, but that flea was so tarnacious heavy, it couldn't jump without the aid of a Pogo stick.

SEPTEMBER

This is a good month to watch for migrating birds. If you're lucky you might see a balloon-bellied gobbleholer, though it's a mite rare.

You can tell the gobbleholer from its flight. It doesn't migrate north and south like other wing flappers — it travels east and west.

It feeds on doughnut holes, mostly.

Last spring our young'uns found an orphaned gobbleholer — newborn. They tried to feed it a doughnut hole, but the bird was too small to tackle a grown-up meal like that.

"It'll starve," cried Little Clarinda.

Well, the young'uns weren't going to let that happen! They offered the little bird pinholes, and it gobbled them up.

Before long the fledgling was taking on more solid food — moth holes and even the holes in our socks.

"That's a mighty useful bird to have around," I said. "But I wouldn't let the neighbors know you're raising up a balloon-bellied gobbleholer. They might try to shoot it down."

Truth is, gobbleholers are considered a farm pest. Doughnut holes don't exactly stick to the ribs, and the bigger those birds get, the more they need to eat. A full-grown flock came through here two years ago — and mercy! Quicker'n you could swallow a chaw of tobacco they gobbled up an entire row of new-dug postholes.

By midsummer, the young'uns' pet was bigger'n a balloon, and still growing. We just couldn't keep it in doughnut holes. It would go scavaging for knotholes and rabbit holes — and that gave me an idea.

"Willjillhesterchesterpeterpollytimtommarylarryand-littleclarinda!" I called. "It's mighty dangerous having this carrot-drilled, clear-to-China hole on our farm. Help me move off the chicken wire — and don't fall in."

Well! We'd no more got the hole uncovered than the bird came running over. It tapped its beak into the hole a time or two, and seemed to like the flavor.

Down it went, its wings buzzing like a hummingbird's. That creature burned up energy almost as fast as it could eat.

What a feast! I don't know how deep the bird went. It

made no more sound than the hum of a gnat at fifty miles.

As the days passed I began to fear the gobbleholer might overeat and explode. They've been known to do that, which is why they're so rare — almost extinct.

Finally, the balloon-bellied bird ate its way back to the top and surfaced on the sixteenth of September — this month.

It did a mighty neat job of patching up that hole. It wiped its bill on the fresh earth, cocked its head, and seemed to give us a fond, last look.

Migration was stirring in its soul, and off it took — due west.

It had grown so big — well, I reckon that's why it didn't get shot down. Farmers mistook it for an ostrich that had learned to fly.

Reports came in from the entire length of its flight. And the mystery of why the balloon-bellied gobbleholer migrates west was solved!

The young'uns' pet was spotted setting down in a canyon to do its winter feeding.

The Grand Canyon.

McPROVERB

Birds of a feather that flock together make a good target.

Hester McBroom's
Surefire Cure for Homework

FARM *TIP*

To grow frozen peas, plant together with iceberg lettuce.

OCTOBER

Freeze & thaw & sunshine fickle —
Mercury rides a Pogo stickle.

How to Rid a Barn of Rats

Make up a couple of dozen artificial rat holes. Cut them out of black paper. See illustration 1.

Paste them along the bottom boards of the barn. Rats will run into the artificial holes and bang their heads. See illustration 2.

The varmints will get tired of this after a while and skedaddle. See illustration 3.

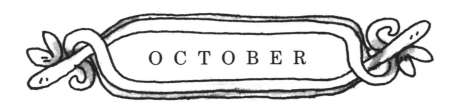

Here it is October and our hens still haven't laid an egg.

For months now, every time I've gone out to the chicken house, the nests have turned up empty. Our hens have plumb forgot the art of laying eggs.

They strut about, fat and sassy, and well-fed. Not only have they had shelled corn to eat, but during the summer months they snapped up all the bugs and insects they could find.

Now, chickens are not too bright, but you wouldn't think they'd forget a simple thing like laying an egg.

"Maybe they're under a spell," said Mary.

"I don't believe in spells," I answered.

Peter came along. "Reckon we'd better get busy, Pa, if we're going to grow any pumpkins this year."

"Plenty of time," I said. "Halloween's days off."

The truth is, I don't like to grow pumpkins. Our soil is too thundering rich. We can plant and harvest two or three crops a day. But you have to be mighty quick to pluck 'em off the vines while the pumpkins are still small — no more'n four feet across. Folks just won't buy the big ones.

But Halloween is Halloween. I took my mind off our ungrateful, nonlaying hens, and we planted our wonderful one-acre farm in pumpkins.

My, didn't those vines lead us a breathless chase! *Whoosh!* They grew so fast they sounded like Roman candles. *Shoooh!* We ran this way and that to chop off the pumpkins.

But in the confusion, one of 'em got away. The vine curled up a tree. We didn't notice the pumpkin up in the branches until it was too late. It was full-size by then — bigger'n a harvest moon.

"Pa," said Polly. "Can we have it? We could scoop it out and have ourselves a tree house."

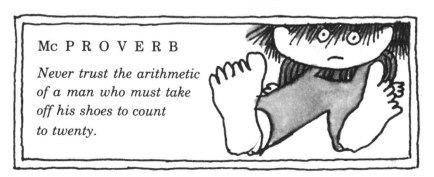

Mc P R O V E R B

Never trust the arithmetic of a man who must take off his shoes to count to twenty.

"A tree house?" Larry said. "We could carve it as a jack-o'-lantern and scare everybody in the county from up there."

"Help yourselves, my lambs," I said.

By nightfall they had that tree house scooped out and a jack-o'-lantern face carved in it. The eyes were big as washtubs and the teeth looked mean as a crocodile's.

They couldn't wait to try it out. After supper they gathered up our lanterns and climbed up into the pumpkin. But before they could fire up the lanterns, Tom came down after me. His hair stood bristling on end.

"Pa — we've seen a ghost. Come quick!"

I climbed the ladder and let myself down inside the pumpkin. "It's a mite early for Halloween ghosts," I said.

"Then that one's got its days mixed," whispered Polly, pointing. "See it, Pa?"

The thing was over in the chicken yard. It glowed something fearful, and I felt my scalp prickle.

The ghost was stooping over and collecting a basket of eggs. *Eggs?*

They glowed like moonlight, and suddenly I had the answer to our nonlaying chickens.

"Young'uns," I whispered. "Light all the lanterns!"

A moment later that huge jack-o'-lantern showed its monster face in the tree.

The ghost looked up. It gave a yelp and tore out of the chicken yard.

That haunt had the fright of its life! Eggs flew out of the basket as it ran, spattering and shining on the ground.

I hurried down the ladder and followed the trail of glowing spots. I pulled up short at Heck Jones's place.

"Heck Jones!" I called at the windows. "You're a con-founded egg thief!"

"Hee-haw!" he answered. "Prove it!"

"I will! In the courthouse!"

The next day I hauled him up before the judge. "Your Honor," I said. "I owe my hens an apology. I calculated they'd stopped laying. Nothing of the sort! It's clear, Your Honor, they ate so many lightning bugs this summer their eggs glow. And Heck Jones has eaten so many of our eggs he lights up, too. Put him in a dark closet and see for yourself."

Three minutes later the judge declared him guilty.

Heck Jones was still serving his sentence when Halloween came along. The young'uns lit up their tree house jack-o'-lantern and raised gooseflesh for miles around. It was a howling, scarifying success.

I believe Heck Jones might have been able to see the glow of it from town. The judge had sentenced him to stand on the courthouse corner every night.

He was serving as the town lamppost.

PRAIRIE WILDLIFE

Porcupine Trout

This unfriendly fish uses its quills to knit fishnets: they catch and devour one another. Becoming extinct.

WEATHER SIGN

It's not a sign of an uncommon winter when ducks and geese fly south. But, if your chickens flap their wings and try to join them, winter will be infernally cold. And if the ducks and geese carry one-way tickets — look out!

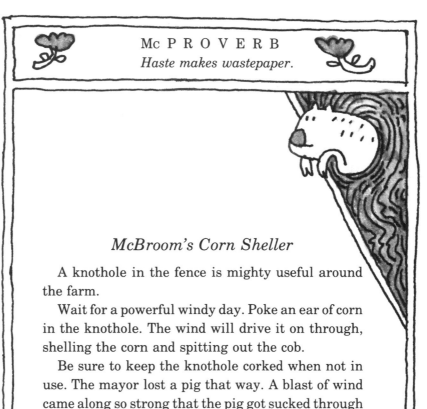

Mc **P R O V E R B**
Haste makes wastepaper.

McBroom's Corn Sheller

A knothole in the fence is mighty useful around the farm.

Wait for a powerful windy day. Poke an ear of corn in the knothole. The wind will drive it on through, shelling the corn and spitting out the cob.

Be sure to keep the knothole corked when not in use. The mayor lost a pig that way. A blast of wind came along so strong that the pig got sucked through the knothole and came out pork sausages.

NOVEMBER

Fahrenheit in br-r-r-r r degrees!
Gravity itself will freeze!

A World Record

The temperature fell so low this month that there wasn't a suit of red woolen underwear anywhere on the prairie. It all turned blue from the cold.

NOVEMBER

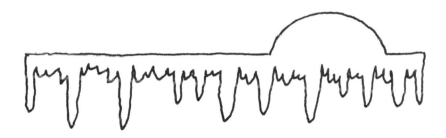

We had no November this year. It was so dreadful cold
the sun froze below the horizon and wouldn't budge an
inch. The air didn't thaw until December 1. There came
a crack of dawn, and the days started up again.

Mc P R O V E R B

It's good luck to find a penny.
It's better luck to find
a ten-dollar bill.

WEATHER SIGN

When squirrels put in a large hoard of nuts, expect a hard
winter. But if the varmints steal your nutcracker, it just
means they're planning a party.

NATURE LORE

Feed a cow shelled peanuts
and she will give peanut butter.

Goat's Milk

Pa bought a nanny goat
with eyes as soft as silk.
She ate our pie plates yesterday,
and today gave cans of milk.

— Peter McBroom

78

DECEMBER

Lightning, thunder: wizard's skies!
(Will it snow? Will it won't?)
Keep the year before your eyes —
Now you see it, now you (   )!

PRAIRIE WILDLIFE

The Prairie Woolabout

An endangered species. This is a wild sheep with a reversible hide. When the temperature dips to forty-three degrees below zero, the woolabout begins to feel a mite chilly. It sheds its coat and puts it back on with the woolly fleece inside.

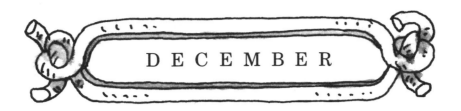

Thunder, snow, hail, and head-scratching puzzlement —
that's December out here on the farm.

Puzzlement? Thinking up Christmas gifts for eleven
young'uns keeps my dear wife Melissa and me scratching
our heads.

"Every year they wish for bicycles," she said.

I nodded my head sadly. "But we can't afford eleven
bicycles. What a conpuzzlement!"

She was knitting yellow socks out of yarn as thick as
rope. I hoped they weren't for me.

The young'uns were busy themselves, making gifts
and wrapping them and trying to keep their secrets.

On the farm they'd learned not to let anything go to waste. On a banging, rumbling, thundering day, I saw Polly set out six bottles with a funnel stuck in each one. I didn't ask what she was up to.

And after a hailstorm came along, several of the young'uns rummaged through the stones. Out here on the prairie, the hail is large gauge. Heck Jones has been known to drill finger holes in the smaller ones and sell them as bowling balls.

On the day before Christmas, Melissa and I were still scratching our heads.

"Hang the cost," I said. "I'm going to town."

A shiny blue bike stood in the window of the hardware store. I went inside and said, "I'll take eleven of 'em, gift wrapped."

The storekeeper, Gnat Wilson, shook his head. "Only got the one in the window."

"Better than none," I said, knowing the young'uns would do a mighty lot of scrapping over it. "I'll take the thing."

He gift wrapped it with his best butcher paper, and I started for home. Dark falls early this time of year, and I reckoned I could sneak it in the barn. But I could hear the young'uns in there working on last-minute gifts. I leaned the bicycle against a fence post. I'd go back for it later.

A whistle of wind came along while we were singing carols. And then snowflakes the size of pancakes began to spatter against the windows. By time the young'uns went to bed a full-blown blizzard had whipped in.

I hurried outside to fetch the bicycle, but it had blown over and was already under three feet of snow. I tried digging for it, but for every shovelful I dug out, two more blew in. It would have to wait till morning.

The morning rang out with cries of "Merry Christmas!" When we lifted the shades to look outside — there was no outside. We were snowed in.

But nothing can dampen a Christmas morning. We opened our gifts. There were screams of joy and jollification. What surprises!

Jill had used yarn to make stitch marks in a hailstone, and gave it to Will as a winter baseball. Polly gave Peter and Tim and Tom the bottles she'd set with funnels. She'd corked in the banging, rumbling thunder. Didn't the boys make a ruckus with those homemade prairie popguns!

Later, we climbed out through an attic window. The blizzard had passed, leaving a fall of snow so deep that if I lied about it, I'd be telling the truth.

"My lambs," I said. "Looks like we're all going to have to dig for your Christmas present."

It was hours before we uncovered the fence post where

I'd leaned the bicycle. The wind had not only blown over the two-wheeler, it had ripped away the butcher paper.

When I caught sight of the shiny blue bike, I jumped in the air and clicked my heels. What a heart-thumping fine Christmas surprise! Our wonderful topsoil had been at work. The two-wheeler had stretched out considerable. There'd be no bickering among the young'uns. They feasted their eyes on a *bicycle built for eleven!*

Oh, didn't they climb on in a hurry! They rode about through the snow, laughing and screaming, and hardly wanting to come in for Christmas dinner.

Inside the house, I was almighty surprised to find Heck Jones seated at the table. He was all dressed up in his starched choke-me-to-death collar.

Dear Melissa! She couldn't bear the thought of letting him eat alone.

"Here's a present from all of us, Heck Jones," she said, and handed him a large package all done up in ribbons.

I don't mind saying he choked up a bit. And when he opened the package and drew up a pair of whopping-big, hand-knit socks, he dabbed at his eyes with them.

"Just my size," he said.

When the evening was over, I turned to Melissa. "That was a mighty kind thing to do, my love. But how's he going to get his shoes over those socks? The yarn's thick as a swollen thumb."

Melissa smiled happily. "Josh, you know he's so tall that he has to sleep with his feet sticking out the windows. That's why he's always been so mean — his feet are cold. With these socks, he'll be a changed man."

For the next few nights we noticed Heck Jones's feet

sticking out the windows in those sleeping socks. And I declare if on the last day of the year he didn't invite me to meet him in town for a friendly game of horseshoes.

"Ten o'clock suit you, Josh?" he asked with a smile.

"I'll be there, Heck."

Wasn't he a changed man!

I reached town in plenty of time, though it was kind of hard to find. It lay in a hollow, and the blizzard had buried everything but the church steeples.

I practiced pitching horseshoes around an iron post sticking up through the snow. Finally, Heck showed up riding his boney nag of a horse. He was a mite late — it was near noon by then.

"I'll bet you a month of Sunday dinners I can beat you hands down," he said. "If I lose, Josh, I'll expect you to bring the whole family."

"That's mighty neighborly," I said, and agreed.

"Let's trade horseshoes to keep the game honest."

"Square and fair," I said, and handed over my horseshoes.

He began pitching at once, and made a ringer.

"Splendid, Heck," I said. "But I can beat it. Now let me borrow your horseshoes. Where are they?"

"Over there."

"Over where?"

"On my horse — pitch 'em if you can. Hee-haw, McBroom! What time is dinner?"

He rode off laughing. I sat on the iron post, choking mad. Steam must have shot out of my ears. The only thing changed about Heck Jones was his collar.

I finally got up and trudged for home.

It was only after the snow melted that I discovered I'd been sitting on the top of a flagpole.

McBROOM'S WONDERFUL ONE-ACRE FARM

Stuff For Sale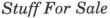

McBroom's Natural Winter Extract & Relief for the Summer Dismals

Made from pure & genuine prairie wind. Healthful. Restores vigor & promotes sleep on hot summer nights. Uncorked, the wind can be used to blow-dry your hair. Comes in plain, barnyard, or pine scented.

Prairie Dog Holes
Special Offer

Buy six and get one free! Saves you the work of digging post holes. Or use to plant trees. Carefully packed to avoid breakage.

McBroom's Insect Repellent

Giant flour sifter. When mosquitos, gnats, and other varmints are bad, stand on roof and sift down a white storm of flour. The insects will mistake it for snow, and freeze to death.

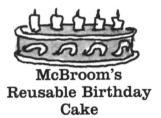

McBroom's Reusable Birthday Cake

Available in hard winters only. Comes complete with lit candles — the flames frozen stiff. Relatives can't blow them out, and give up on the cake. Save for next birthday on the calendar, and use again. Great for large families.

BARBED WIRE IN DECORATOR COLORS

Our own secret formula. Makes cows so contented they give more milk. And pretties up your farm at the same time. Specify beige, chartreuse, or avocado.